THE
low carb
COOKBOOK

GINA STEER

p

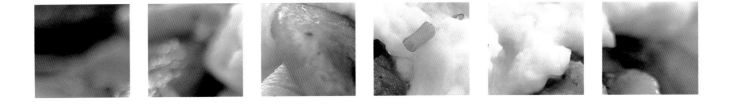

This is a Parragon Book
First published in 2004

Parragon
Queen Street House
4 Queen Street
Bath
BA1 1HE
UK

Designed and produced by
THE BRIDGEWATER BOOK COMPANY

Introduction, Nutritional Analyses and Facts: *Charlotte Watts*
Photography: *Clive Bozzard-Hill*
Home Economist: *Philippa Vanstone*
Stylist: *Angela Macfarlane*

The publishers would like to thank the following companies for the loan
of props: *Dartington Crystal, Marlux Mills, Maxwell & Williams, Lifestyle Collections,
Viners & Oneida, Typhoon and John Lewis.*

Printed in China

ISBN 1-40544-585-8

NOTES FOR THE READER

This book uses metric and imperial measurements. Follow the same units
of measurement throughout; do not mix metric and imperial. All spoon
measurements are level, unless otherwise stated: teaspoons are assumed
to be 5 ml and tablespoons are assumed to be 15 ml.

Individual vegetables such as potatoes are medium and pepper is freshly
ground black pepper. Milk used in the recipes is skimmed or semi-skimmed
to help limit the fat content of the meal. The recipes have been made with
a reduced-fat and -sugar content in accordance with healthy eating guidelines.
However, this means that they will not keep fresh for as long a period of
time as their higher-fat and -sugar alternatives. This is particularly the case
with cakes, so storage advice has been included where appropriate.

Some of the recipes require stock. If you use commercially made stock
granules or cubes, these can have a relatively high salt content, so do not
add any further salt. If you make your own stock, keep the fat and salt content
to a minimum. Don't fry the vegetables before simmering – just simmer the
vegetables, herbs and meat, poultry or fish in water and strain. Meat and
poultry stocks should be strained, cooled and refrigerated before use so that
the fat from the meat rises to the top and solidifies – it can then be easily
removed and this reduces the saturated fat content of the meal. Homemade
stocks should be stored in the refrigerator and used within two days, or frozen
in usable portions and labelled.

Ovens should be preheated to the specified temperature. If using a fan-
assisted oven, check the manufacturer's instructions for adjusting the time
and temperature.

The values of the nutritional analysis for each recipe refer to a single
serving, or a single slice where relevant. They do not include the serving
suggestion. Where a range of portions is given the nutritional analysis figure
refers to the mid-range figure. The calorific value given is in KCal (Kilocalories).
The carbohydrate figure includes starches and sugars, with the sugar value
then given separately. The fat figure is likewise the total fat, with the saturated
part then given separately.

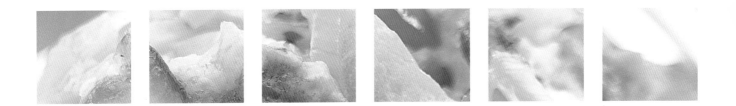

contents

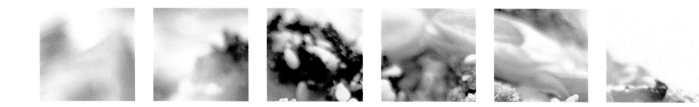

Introduction

There have been several widely adopted 'dieting' trends over the last 30–40 years, but none has affected to the same degree the way that people approach weight loss as the high-protein, low-carbohydrate diet made so popular in recent times. The aim of this book is to put the basic principles underlying that weight-loss programme into practice in a range of recipes which constitute a sensible eating plan, while avoiding the well-documented health risks hitherto associated with this particular dietary approach.

A significant proportion of people today are showing symptoms and conditions associated with poor blood-sugar control. This is where the levels of sugar or glucose in the blood become too high from consuming too many or inappropriate kinds of carbohydrate, from over-use of stimulants (caffeine, cigarettes and alcohol) or from an excess of stress. On a day-to-day basis this can lead to weight gain, and also to fatigue, headaches, anxiety, irritability, depression, insomnia, poor memory and concentration and difficulty coping with stress. This sets up a cycle where a slump of blood sugar after the sudden rush from the food or stimulus causes a craving for something else to lift the blood sugar back up again. This is when people turn to caffeine and sugar, which is what the English 'high tea' was invented for since the time it was traditionally served, at 4 pm, is when people often experience a blood-sugar slump and feel the need for a 'fix'.

Continual high blood-sugar levels can have a more serious outcome, leading to high cholesterol, heart disease, obesity and increasing problems with mental function. People who recognize this blood-sugar cycle may have trouble dealing with carbohydrates and the reason for this lies with insulin – see The Role of Insulin (opposite). In this case, they may be suited to a diet that contains fewer starches and grains, especially if they are also experiencing digestive problems. The best advice is to experiment by omitting these foods and seeing how the body reacts.

Many people find that lowering carbohydrate intake helps them lose weight, but this does not have to involve increasing protein and saturated fat intake to potentially dangerous levels. A diet that prioritizes some lean meat, vegetable proteins, low-sugar vegetables and beneficial oils can have many far-reaching health benefits, and people often feel generally much cleaner, lighter and more efficient on this type of diet. But you are the best judge of how you feel, and learning to listen to your body's needs is an important part of becoming healthier. These dietary guidelines can, in any case, help you to manage your weight, in conjunction with a suitable exercise programme and a controlled daily calorie intake. The recipes are also delicious, which is a very important factor in sustaining your commitment to a healthy diet.

Insulin Sensitivity

Too much insulin can also lead to insulin sensitivity, where the body loses the ability to recognize insulin or to use it properly and consequently levels in the bloodstream remain too high. This has been linked to a condition called Syndrome X, which has associated weight gain, increased body hair, high cholesterol and heart disease risk.

The Healthy Low-Carbohydrate Approach

Many people have thrived on a diet that is high in protein and without carbohydrates because they have cut out foods that their body has been unable to deal with such as sugars and grains. The problem with massively increasing protein intake is that protein creates acidity in the body, which takes a lot of energy and nutrients to adjust, as it needs to operate in a slightly alkaline state. This response is associated with bone loss, as the alkalizing mineral calcium is taken by the body from bone to buffer this acidity. The high saturated fat foods that are also high protein such as meat and meat products are also associated with heart disease.

Rather than eat too much protein, it is important to consume exactly the right amount, as well as the appropriate types of carbohydrate and fat. Fats and oils are very important for our health but unfortunately in recent times they have been lumped together into one 'bad' category. Fat in the form of oils that do not clog the arteries is used to make all cell membranes, keep skin supple and produce hormones, and is also very efficiently burned as a fuel. Low-carbohydrate diets aim to switch our major fuel-burning substance from carbohydrate to fat, meaning that our bodies store less, burn that which we have stored and become more efficient. Stored fat is the major heart disease risk, since it can easily reach the arteries. It is important to understand that it is not fat itself which is stored as fat. It is excess carbohydrates that are not used as energy which are converted to fat. This is because the body has no other use for them and insulin has to remove them quickly from the bloodstream.

The Role of Insulin

We have many hormones in the body that raise blood-sugar levels, but only one to lower it – insulin. Our bodies were designed to need high blood sugar only in the advent of danger, in the 'fight or flight' response, to provide us with energy in the muscles to deal with an enemy. Stress mimics this response, but in general we don't need to respond so physically to the modern-day anxieties we experience, and so our bodies are left with the task of bringing down these artificially high levels of blood sugar. Along with a diet higher than ever in sugar and carbohydrates, this means that we also have to produce larger amounts of insulin than we should. This can exhaust the pancreas and even eventually lead to Type II diabetes.

This book aims to offer a diet in which, rather than cutting out carbohydrates entirely, you can safely consume them in a way that does not raise your insulin levels and therefore cause weight gain and other adverse symptoms.

The Macronutrients

This is the collective term for carbohydrates, fats and proteins, so-called because they are much larger molecules than vitamins and minerals. The name 'carbohydrate' comes from its components – carbon, hydrogen and oxygen – and it is burned at an easy rate of 4.1 kilocalories per gram. Fat has the same components yet in a different, insoluble form, but can be broken down to be burned as fuel. We are designed to burn fat in cold climates, as it is a compact, dense form of energy (at 9.4 kilocalories per gram), and save carbohydrates for lean times when we need to store fat to burn later. Proteins contain carbon, hydrogen, oxygen and also nitrogen, and are needed to form hormones, enzymes, neurotransmitters, antibodies and structures in the body such as tissues, muscles, bones, skin and hair. We don't want to burn this as a primary fuel as these structures would be affected, but it can be burned at 5.7 kilocalories per gram.

It is partly the low calorific value of carbohydrates that have led to their popularity in the slimming world, and to the detriment of fats. However, for our ancestors, the calorific values of food, meaning the actual energy that the body can obtain from certain foods, was all-important: it was much more preferable for them to find less food but with a higher calorific content. Compared to modern lifestyles and diet, they expended more energy and ate leaner meats, a greater proportion of 'good' fats from nuts, seeds and fish, hardly any grains and no sugar, except that found in fruit. Many people's bodies are still craving for this dietary approach for optimal health.

Carbohydrates

Carbohydrates are not just found in grains and starches like potatoes and other roots but also in vegetables, fruit and dairy products. Carbohydrates are made from simple sugars, which can all break down to glucose eventually, but some are in more complicated forms that take longer to release their sugars into the bloodstream. It is now recognized that it is the type of carbohydrate to be consumed that should be considered and the all-important speed in which it breaks down into the glucose components in the body. Vegetables are the most acceptable form in which to eat carbohydrates, as they are also good sources of antioxidant nutrients (vitamins A, C and E and carotenoids) which protect us from damage from energy production (our exhaust fumes), environmental factors like sunlight and pollution and any harmful components in the food that we eat. They will also provide the carbohydrates we need to make our DNA.

Refined carbohydrates or sugars are very simple molecules. What we call 'sugar' for cooking and eating is actually sucrose – just two molecules of glucose that offer a very quick supply of sugar to the bloodstream, demanding a high need for insulin that can lead to insulin insensitivity and eventually levels of sugar in the blood that are too high. These are found in processed foods, sweets, cakes, soft drinks, fruit juices and very refined carbohydrates such as white bread, where the bran part of the wheat has been stripped away. This quick release of sugar can be laid down as fat if the equivalent energy is not expended, i.e. if you don't go for a two-mile walk every time you eat a cake.

Complex carbohydrates release their sugars more slowly, so are used for energy rather than laid down as fat. These are termed starches. They also contain fibre, which also helps to slow down sugar release and eliminate toxins from the body to help prevent disease. The wholegrain bran part of cereal grains that is removed in white flour and processed foods contains fibre and provides glucose molecules that are bound together in more complex structures. Vegetables and fruit in their natural, raw state provide complex carbohydrates bound in fibre. They therefore take much more time to break down into their simple sugars and provide a more slow and steady release into the bloodstream.

The carbohydrate issue is, however, not as simple as previously thought – see the Glycaemic Index (pages 10–11).

Grains

Human beings only began eating grains when they changed from being hunter-gatherers to farmers, which in historical terms was relatively recently. Carbohydrates make up about 90 per cent of the world's food supply, the top ten being wheat, maize, rice, barley, soya beans, cane sugar, sorghum, potatoes, oats and cassava. Of these, half are grains, and it is ironic that many people may find that these affect their blood sugar and insulin levels adversely. Many people have wheat and gluten (the protein in wheat, rye, oats and barley) intolerance due to them being difficult to digest and because of the mere fact that they are so prevalent in our diets; we were designed to eat a variety of foods over different seasons and can suffer overload from a diet of toast, sandwiches and cereals. You may

have more of a problem with wheat or other grains than other carbohydrates and you should suspect an intolerance if you have digestive problems, headaches, fatigue, bloating and joint pain on top of the other symptoms of poor blood-sugar balance. You can try eliminating these grains to monitor symptoms, but this can be confusing as the effects of an intolerance can sometimes manifest days after eating the food – consult a nutritionist for further advice. If you are cutting out grains, eat a range of vegetables, nuts and pulses to obtain appropriate amounts of fibre and B vitamins.

Fibre

Fibre can either be soluble or insoluble fibre. Each has its different properties, so both are important in the diet and a balance is needed. Fibre helps to level out blood sugar by slowing down digestion and the release of sugar from food. Aim for 35 grams per day to balance blood sugar, lower cholesterol levels, cleanse the colon of toxins and to help prevent heart disease.

Soluble fibre tends to be found in fruit and vegetables, especially apples, citrus fruits, carrots, cherries, avocados, beetroot, dried apricots and prunes, and also some seed husks such as linseed, oat bran and psyllium husks, which many people take to counter constipation. It helps digestion by absorbing water and softening stools, and this can help lower cholesterol. You should aim to obtain soluble fibre by eating as many different vegetables as possible, as well as some dark fruits and berries.

Insoluble fibre remains undigested and so clears the digestive system, prevents constipation, lessens the incidence of colon and rectal cancer and speeds up the elimination of waste from the body. It is found in brown rice (the fibre is removed when processed to white), rye bread and crackers, lentils, asparagus, Brussels sprouts, cabbage, other wholegrains and fibrous vegetables. When eating smaller amounts of grains, you need to compensate by eating more of these fibrous vegetables.

Vegetables and fruit contain cellulose, an insoluble plant fibre that contains little sugar, but it is important to remember that when cooked these become more readily broken down

into sugars. This is why vegetables such as carrots, peppers and parsnips taste sweeter the longer they are cooked. Raw vegetables are much more beneficial on the whole. Some fruit can be eaten as a good source of nutrients and soluble fibre, but choose less sweet varieties such as grapes, pineapple and bananas and darker, tarter fruits that release sugar less quickly such as berries, cherries, plums and sharp, green apples instead of sweet, red ones. Fruit juices are already broken down into more simple sugars and have had the fibre removed. Your taste buds can guide you – think, for instance, how much sweeter white bread tastes than brown; if you chew a piece for a few minutes, you will taste pure maltose, the sugar that is its main component. See the Glycaemix Index on pages 10–11 for further guidance.

Fats

If you lower your intake of the carbohydrates that can cause the accumulation of body fat, make sure that you include the beneficial oils and essential fats that can produce energy, lower cholesterol and help blood-sugar regulation. It is important to know which oils are best and how they should be used.

Saturated fats tend to be from animal sources, such as butter and meat fats. Solid at room temperature, they can form in the same way in the body. If eaten in high amounts, they can clog arteries and add to the risk of heart disease. Combined with sugars, they can be laid down as fat. Foods containing both, such as pastries, are the main culprits of weight gain.

Monounsaturated fats are vegetable in origin and those traditionally eaten in Mediterranean countries, namely olive, almond, hazelnut, peanut and avocado oils. They contain a fatty acid called oleic acid or omega-9 and remain liquid at room temperature but begin to solidify when refrigerated. These have been found to have a neutral effect on blood cholesterol, although an excess can raise fat levels in the blood. The exception is olive oil, which has been shown actually to reduce blood cholesterol. However, this effect is thought to be caused by unique active components rather than the monounsaturated fat content. These are less damaged by heat than oils that stay liquid at room temperature and therefore can be used for cooking at low to medium temperatures.

Polyunsaturated fatty acids are always liquid and contain the essential fatty acids, the omega-6 oils, that help to produce localized hormones in the body, which are important for blood sugar and cholesterol regulation and heart health. These include sesame, soya, sunflower, walnut, pumpkin and hemp oils. They are termed 'essential' because they are crucial to body functions and must be consumed as they cannot be made in the body. Saturated fats can actually stop essential fats being used at a cellular level. These should be used cold for dressings and dips as they are very susceptible to damage from heat.

With both polyunsaturated and monounsaturated fats, eating the nuts, seeds and vegetables from which these oils are produced can also play a vital role in blood-sugar management. For example, avocados contain not only beneficial oils but high levels of nutrients and soluble fibre, and plant sterols (types of fat) which help to reduce bad cholesterol. Although avocados, olives, nuts and seeds also contain some saturated fats and should be eaten in moderation, they provide omega-6 oils, vitamin E, vitamins B_3 and B_6, zinc and magnesium, which all aid blood-sugar management.

Omega-3 oils are those found in oily fish such as salmon, tuna, herring, mackerel, trout and sardines. Like the omega-6 oils, these are essential fatty acids and are crucial to our health. Much research has shown how important these are for heart health and they should be eaten 3–4 times a week, in variety. Both omega-3 and omega-6 oils protect parts of the body that are rich in fats – the eyes, kidneys and liver – as well as the circulation from the heart. For vegetarians, hemp, pumpkin, soya and walnut oils contain some omega-3 oils but are higher in omega-6. Omega-3 and omega-6 should be eaten in a one-to-one ratio and flax or linseed can be added to food as a source of omega-3 oils.

Proteins

Proteins are the major source of building materials for the body. They can also be used as a source of energy that is released very slowly. They are therefore very good for blood-sugar management and can slow down sugar release into the bloodstream if eaten with less complex carbohydrates.

Many people do not eat enough proteins to sustain the body's structural needs, especially at breakfast time when the body is setting up its supply for the demands of the day. Caution should be taken, however, not to obtain these mainly from high-fat sources such as meats, but additionally from eggs, low-fat dairy products and vegetable sources such as pulses, peas and beans, and in small amounts from other vegetables such as broccoli, cauliflower and asparagus. Too much protein can create excess acidity in the body. Protein requirements can be as low as 35 g for smaller women to up to 200 g a day for a heavily exercising athlete, but generally proteins should account for 30 per cent of your daily calorie intake. You may have a higher need if you exercise often, but you then need to counter this extra acidity with more vegetables to alkalize your body.

The Glycaemic Index

Research into sugars and their release into the bloodstream has found that some foods behave in a surprising way when introduced into the body. It is no longer enough just to distinguish between simple sugars and complex carbohydrates. As we are unable to predict how a food will act by its sugar and starch content alone, the Glycaemic Index has been drawn up to compare the release of sugar into the bloodstream that foods create against a measure of 100 for glucose. In the table on the right, foods are categorized into high, medium and low. High (more than 70) means that sugars are released very quickly, near to the speed of glucose itself. These foods should not be eaten on their own as this can cause a quick increase of blood sugar. They can, however, be eaten in small amounts at the same time as a food with a low score (under 55). This would equal a combined score in the medium range (55–70) and a good control of blood sugar. You should aim to include as many foods in the low range as possible for the best blood-sugar control and include those in the medium or high categories only with protein or other low-GI foods.

A low-GI diet can help to increase the body's sensitivity to insulin, so that the insulin you have works more effectively and you are less likely to become insensitive to it. A low-GI diet can also, in conjunction with a low-saturated fat diet, help to keep blood fats low and therefore reduce heart disease-related risks.

Knowing the GI values of foods is very useful in keeping your actual carbohydrate load in check as you may be getting more sugar straight into the bloodstream than you expected from certain foods. For instance, note that corn flakes and parsnips have very high scores and should be eaten very sparingly with foods that bring the score down overall. Proteins and oils are not included in the Glycaemic Index as they are known to be low-GI foods since they do not contain carbohydrates. They can, therefore, be eaten

Low-GI Foods – below 55

Fruit and Fruit Juices

Cherries	22
Grapefruit	25
Dried apricots	31
Pears	37
Apples	38
Plums	39
Apple juice	41
Peaches	42
Oranges	44
Grapes	46
Pineapple juice	46
Grapefruit juice	48
Orange juice	52
Kiwi fruit	53
Banana	54

Vegetables

Broccoli	10
Cabbage	10
Lettuce	10
Mushrooms	10
Raw onions	10
Raw red peppers	10
Raw carrots	49
Sweet potatoes	54

Grains

Pearl barley	31
Rye	34
Brown basmati rice	52

Breads

Mixed grain bread	48
Pumpernickel rye bread	50

Pasta

Vermicelli	35
Linguine	42
Instant noodles	47

Bakery Products

Sponge cake (made with egg)	46

Breakfast Cereals

Bran cereal	42

Dairy

Low-fat yogurt	14
Full-fat milk	27
Skimmed milk	27
Low-fat fruit yogurt	33
Custard	43

Legumes

Soya beans	14
Red split lentils	18
Green lentils	29
Canned chickpeas	42
Canned pinto beans	45
Canned baked beans	48
Green peas	48

Medium-GI Foods – 55–70

Fruit and Fruit Juices

Mangoes	56
Sultanas	56
Apricots	57
Raisins	64
Pineapple	66

Vegetables

Sweetcorn	55
New potatoes	57
Beetroot	64
Boiled or mashed potatoes	70

Grains

White basmati rice	58
Buckwheat	55
Brown rice	55

Breads

White pitta bread	58
Hamburger bun	61
Rye flour bread	64
High-fibre wheat bread	68
Wholemeal wheat bread	69

Pasta

Durum wheat spaghetti	55

Bakery Products

Pastry	59
Muffin	62
Croissant	67
Crumpet	69

Breakfast Cereals

Muesli	56
Porridge	61
Spun wheat biscuit	69
Wheat biscuits	70

Biscuits

Oatmeal biscuits	55
Tea biscuits	55
Digestive biscuits	59
Shortbread	64

Savoury Biscuits

Wheat thins	67

Dairy

Ice cream	61

Sugars

High-fruit jam	55
Honey	58
Table sugar	64

Sweets and Snacks

Popcorn	55

Beverages

Orange cordial	66
Fizzy orange	68

High-GI Foods – above 70

Fruit and Fruit Juices

Watermelon	72

Vegetables

Swede	72
Chips	75
Pumpkin	75
Baked potatoes	85
Cooked carrots	85
Parsnips	97

Grains

White rice	88

Breads

White bagel	72
White wheat bread	78
Gluten-free bread	90
French baguette	95

Bakery Products

Doughnuts	76
Waffles	76

Breakfast Cereals

Wheat bran flakes with added dried fruit	71
Puffed wheat	74
Crisped rice	82
Corn flakes	83

Savoury Biscuits and Crackers

Water biscuits	71
Rice cakes	77
Puffed crispbread	81

Sweets and Snacks

Corn tortillas	74
Jelly beans	80
Pretzels	81
Dates	99

Beverages

High-glucose sports drinks	95

Legumes

Broad beans	79

with the high-GI foods to slow down sugar release, for instance lean chicken with parsnips or low-GI nuts with corn flakes. This approach has been used in this book to create low- and medium-GI recipes that may still contain small amounts of high-GI foods but will not raise blood-sugar levels beyond the 'normal' range by combining for average scores. Some 'treat' foods such as ice cream and biscuits have surprisingly low GI scores, but this is often due to their high fat content and they should still be eaten sparingly.

General Dietary Advice

Eat as many raw fruits and vegetables and fresh vegetable juices as you can where practical. This ensures a slow release of sugar into the bloodstream, and the intake of beneficial insoluble fibre and nutrient-dense foods. Lightly cook vegetables and make these the mainstay of your carbohydrate intake, paying attention to the GI scores on pages 10–11.

A healthy low-carbohydrate diet minimizes the inclusion of foods high in starchy carbohydrates (potatoes and cooked root vegetables), and grains and cereals (wheat, oats, bread, pasta, noodles, couscous and bulgar wheat). Beans, peas and pulses contain starchy carbohydrates but also good amounts of protein and fibre and so should be included in your diet.

The most important factor is to avoid foods that are high in sugary carbohydrates – these include the usual demons such as chocolate, biscuits, muffins, cakes and so on.

Foods that contain nutrients needed for blood-sugar balance (zinc, magnesium, vitamins B_3, B_6 and C) are nuts, seeds, fish, dark green vegetables, brassicas, pulses, beans, peas, eggs, avocados, oats, onions and asparagus. These foods are also important for managing cholesterol levels and lowering the

risk of heart disease. Avoiding stimulants (caffeine, alcohol and cigarettes) helps to eliminate 'highs and lows' of blood sugar and reduce sugar cravings.

About the Recipes

When putting together the recipes in this book, practicality and ease were important factors. Choices were made to provide you with an accessible diet that aims to help you feel more healthy and in control of your body. The overall GI score of combinations of foods was considered and a rating of either low or medium has been assigned to each recipe. It makes sense for you to prioritize those that are low and eat the medium ones less often, as they will naturally release sugar into your bloodstream more quickly, even if the carbohydrate content appears to be lower. It is also important to vary your diet and the recipes to ensure a good spread of different nutrients in any given week – you can do this by consulting the nutritional information accompanying each recipe.

A nutritional fact is also provided for each recipe, which highlights the specific health benefits of certain foods, for instance in balancing blood sugar, increasing the uptake of insulin, burning fuel more efficiently and therefore reducing weight and the risk of heart disease. Foods that are considered to be of particular benefit for blood-sugar balance are blueberries, cinnamon, chicory, onion, pulses, beans, garlic, olive oil, nuts and avocados. These should be included in your diet often, but remember that a variety of foods is paramount to health, to ensure a full range and balance of nutrients.

Some of the recipes include grains such as rice and couscous as accompaniments. If you wish to try eliminating these to monitor health and symptoms, replace them with additional vegetables and pulses to ensure that you obtain enough fibre and B vitamins.

The choice of specific varieties of ingredients used in the recipes also takes into account their effect on the release of blood sugar. For instance, if rice is featured, brown rice has been chosen as the best option. In the same way, consideration has been given to the choice of oils and types of fibre and carbohydrates, and this is reflected in the nutritional analyses.

Quick Tomato Sauce

Here is a very useful and versatile recipe for tomato sauce, which is also featured in a couple of the following recipes and can be used as an accompaniment to your own favourite recipes. Simply by adding different fresh herbs, a chopped fresh chilli or a dash of balsamic vinegar or wine, the flavour can be adapted to suit whatever dish it accompanies.

SERVES 4–6

1 tbsp olive oil
1–2 garlic cloves, crushed
2 shallots, finely chopped
400 g/14 oz canned chopped tomatoes
150 ml/5 fl oz vegetable stock
2–3 tsp Worcestershire sauce
salt and pepper
1 tbsp chopped fresh basil

Heat the oil in a saucepan over a medium heat, add the garlic and shallots and cook for 3 minutes, stirring frequently. Stir in the tomatoes with their juice, stock, Worcestershire sauce and salt and pepper to taste and bring to the boil. Reduce the heat and simmer for 10–12 minutes, or until a thick sauce consistency is reached. Stir in the basil, taste, adjust the seasoning and serve. For a smoother sauce, process in a food processor or blender and push through a nylon sieve to remove the seeds, if desired.

Calories 44.4   Protein 1.7g   Carbohydrates 2.5g
Sugars 3.6g   Fat 0g   Saturated Fat 0g   GI Medium

We have included a Desserts & Baking section, which may seem a contradiction in terms, but the recipes are relatively low GI and use very little actual sugar. The idea is that you can treat yourself occasionally without abandoning your dietary goals, and it will also help you not to feel that you are missing out. You can ignore this section if your symptoms are acute.

Breakfasts & Brunches

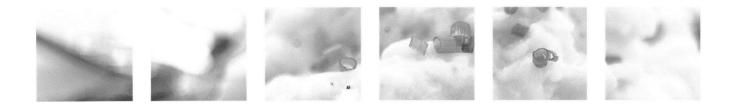

These days there are many passing fads and fashions where food is concerned, all declaring that their approach is the best for optimum health and well-being. But there is no escaping from the simple truth – if you eat a good breakfast, it will keep you going right through the day and avoid the necessity to graze along the way. The following recipes are designed to do just that. All are quick and easy to prepare and suitable for the whole family. Choose, among others, from the traditional Bacon & Tomato Scramble, the refreshing Berry Smoothie or the fragrant Fish Brunch. Whichever you choose, not only will it be extremely tasty but healthily sustaining.

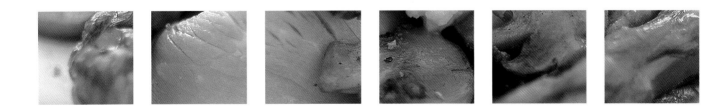

serves 4

Bacon & Tomato Scramble

Ingredients

8 lean back bacon rashers

2 beef or 4 medium tomatoes, halved

4 eggs

3 tbsp milk

salt and pepper

1 tbsp snipped fresh chives

1 tbsp unsalted butter

Nutritional Fact

Eggs contain lecithin, which helps break down fats in the liver, and sulphur, which helps to clear out toxins and alcohol from the liver.

Serving Analysis

• *Calories*	*272*
• *Protein*	*16g*
• *Carbohydrate*	*6.9g*
• *Sugars*	*4.6g*
• *Fat*	*20.5g*
• *Saturates*	*7.5g*
• *GI*	*Low*

1 Preheat the grill to high and cover the grill rack with foil. Arrange the bacon on the foil and cook under the preheated grill for 3–4 minutes on each side, or until crisp. About 3 minutes before the end of cooking time, add the tomatoes, cut-side up, and cook for the remainder of the cooking time.

2 Meanwhile, beat the eggs, milk and salt and pepper to taste in a medium-size bowl, then stir in the chives.

3 Melt the butter in a non-stick saucepan over a medium heat, pour in the egg mixture and cook, stirring gently with a wooden spoon, for 5–6 minutes, or until lightly set.

4 Arrange the egg scramble with the cooked bacon and tomatoes on warmed serving plates and serve immediately. Sprinkle with extra chopped chives, if desired.

serves 1

Berry Smoothie

Nutritional Fact
Berries release their sugars very slowly and their dark colour comes from protective bioflavonoids or plant chemicals, which are good for the circulation and heart health.

Serving Analysis

• Calories	272
• Protein	11g
• Carbohydrate	32g
• Sugars	24g
• Fat	12g
• Saturates	5g
• GI	Low

Ingredients

25 g/1 oz blueberries
85 g/3 oz raspberries, thawed if frozen
1 tsp clear honey
200 ml/7 fl oz live or bio yogurt
about 1 heaped tbsp crushed ice
1 tbsp sesame seeds

1 Put the blueberries into a food processor or blender and process for 1 minute.

2 Add the raspberries, honey and yogurt and process for a further minute.

3 Add the ice and sesame seeds and process again for a further minute.

4 Pour into a tall glass and serve immediately.

serves 6

Nutty Cereal

Ingredients

115 g/4 oz shelled pecans, chopped

115 g/4 oz shelled hazelnuts, chopped

115 g/4 oz flaked almonds

115 g/4 oz no-soak dried apricots

85 g/3 oz sunflower seeds

115 g/4 oz jumbo oats

To serve

freshly sliced banana

strawberries or raspberries

milk

1 Preheat the oven to 190°C/375°F/Gas Mark 5. Spread all the nuts out on a baking sheet and toast in the preheated oven for 12–15 minutes, turning occasionally. Remove from the oven and leave to cool.

2 Meanwhile, finely chop the apricots.

3 Put all the ingredients into a large mixing bowl and mix together. Store in an airtight container.

4 When ready to serve, spoon 2–3 tablespoons into separate serving bowls, top with sliced banana and a few strawberries or raspberries, then pour over a little milk and serve.

Nutritional Fact

Nuts, particularly almonds, are especially good for balancing blood sugar with good levels of most nutrients and omega-6 oils, the essential fatty acids.

Serving Analysis

- Calories   557
- Protein   16g
- Carbohydrate   32g
- Sugars   11g
- Fat   43.5g
- Saturates   3.7g
- GI   Low

serves 2

Piperade

Nutritional Fact

Red and orange peppers contain beta-carotene, a powerful antioxidant that is found in red, yellow and orange vegetables and fruit.

Serving Analysis

• *Calories*	*268*
• *Protein*	*15g*
• *Carbohydrate*	*15g*
• *Sugars*	*8.4g*
• *Fat*	*17g*
• *Saturates*	*3.2g*
• *GI*	*Medium*

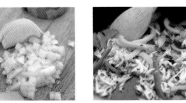

Ingredients

1 tbsp olive oil

1 onion, finely chopped

1–2 garlic cloves, crushed (optional)

1 red pepper, deseeded and cut into thin strips

1 orange pepper, deseeded and cut into thin strips

85 g/3 oz courgette, coarsely grated

4 eggs

3 tbsp cold water

salt and pepper

1 tbsp chopped fresh basil

1 Heat the oil in a non-stick frying pan over a medium heat, add the onion, garlic, if using, and peppers and cook, stirring frequently, for 5 minutes, or until softened. Stir in the courgette.

2 Beat the eggs with the water and salt and pepper to taste in a medium-size bowl, then pour over the onion and pepper mixture. Using a fork or wooden spatula, gently draw the mixture from the edges of the pan into the centre, allowing the uncooked egg to flow to the edges of the pan.

3 When the egg is lightly set, sprinkle the top with the basil and cook for a further 1–2 minutes, or until cooked to your personal preference.

4 Cut into wedges and serve immediately.

serves 2–4 (2 as a light snack or 4 as part of a brunch)

Eggs Florentine

Ingredients

450 g/1 lb fresh spinach leaves, thoroughly washed

salt and pepper

55 g/2 oz unsalted butter

55 g/2 oz button mushrooms, sliced

55 g/2 oz pine kernels, toasted

6 spring onions, chopped

4 eggs

25 g/1 oz plain wholemeal flour

300 ml/10 fl oz milk, warmed

1 tsp prepared English mustard

85 g/3 oz mature Cheddar cheese, grated

Nutritional Fact

Spinach has high levels of all minerals, but also folic acid, an important B vitamin needed for growth and healing. Folic acid is mainly found in leaves and the name comes from the word 'foliage'.

Serving Analysis

- *Calories*   432
- *Protein*   21g
- *Carbohydrate*   17g
- *Sugars*   6.1g
- *Fat*   32g
- *Saturates*   10.5g
- *GI*   Low

1 Preheat the oven to 190°C/375°F/Gas Mark 5. Shake off any excess water from the spinach, put into a large saucepan over a medium heat with only the water clinging to the leaves and sprinkle with a little salt. Cover and cook for 2–3 minutes, or until wilted. Drain, pressing out any excess liquid, then chop.

2 Heat 15 g/$\frac{1}{2}$ oz of the butter in a small saucepan over a medium heat, add the mushrooms and cook for 2 minutes, stirring frequently. Add the pine kernels and spring onions and cook for a further 2 minutes. Remove, season to taste with salt and pepper and scatter over the spinach. Reserve.

3 Meanwhile, fill a frying pan with cold water and bring to the boil, then reduce the heat to a gentle simmer. Carefully break an egg into a cup and slip into the water. Add the remaining eggs and cook for 4–5 minutes, or until set. Carefully remove with a slotted spoon and arrange on top of the spinach mixture.

4 Melt the remaining butter in a saucepan and stir in the flour. Cook for 2 minutes, then remove from the heat and gradually stir in the milk. Return to the heat and cook, stirring constantly, until the mixture comes to the boil and has thickened. Stir in the mustard, then 55 g/2 oz of the cheese. Continue stirring until the cheese has melted. Add salt and pepper to taste, then pour over the eggs, completely covering them. Sprinkle with the remaining cheese.

5 Cook in the preheated oven for 20–25 minutes, or until piping hot and the top is golden brown and bubbling.

serves 4

Scrambled Eggs with Asparagus

Ingredients

55 g/2 oz unsalted butter

115 g/4 oz baby asparagus spears, diagonally sliced

85 g/3 oz button mushrooms, sliced

4 eggs

3 tbsp single cream

salt and pepper

4 thick slices cooked lean ham

1–2 tbsp snipped fresh chives

1 Melt half the butter in a frying pan over a medium heat, add the asparagus and mushrooms and cook, stirring frequently, for 5 minutes, or until softened. Remove from the pan, drain if necessary and keep warm.

2 Beat the eggs with the cream and salt and pepper to taste in a medium-size bowl.

3 Melt the remaining butter in a non-stick saucepan over a medium heat. Pour in the egg mixture and cook, stirring gently with a wooden spoon, for 5–6 minutes, or until lightly set.

4 Arrange the ham on serving plates, top with the asparagus and mushrooms, then the egg scramble. Sprinkle with the chives and serve immediately.

Nutritional Fact
Asparagus is alkalizing, which means that it helps to clear the kidneys and is a good antidote for rich acidic foods such as meat and dairy.

Serving Analysis
- Calories   255
- Protein   16g
- Carbohydrate   3.7g
- Sugars   1.4g
- Fat   20g
- Saturates   10.4g
- GI   Low

serves 2–4 (2 for breakfast or 4 as part of a brunch)

Fluffy Prawn Omelette

Ingredients

115 g/4 oz cooked peeled prawns, thawed if frozen	4 eggs, separated
4 spring onions, chopped	few dashes of Tabasco sauce, to taste
55 g/2 oz courgette, grated	3 tbsp milk
	salt and pepper
	1 tbsp sunflower or olive oil
	25 g/1 oz mature Cheddar cheese, grated

Nutritional Fact
Having a rich protein source such as prawns for breakfast sets up the day for stable blood sugar and energy release.

Serving Analysis
- Calories   157
- Protein   12g
- Carbohydrate   3.2g
- Sugars   2.3g
- Fat   11g
- Saturates   3.5g
- GI   Low

1 Pat the prawns dry with kitchen paper, then mix with the spring onions and courgette in a bowl and reserve.

2 Using a fork, beat the egg yolks with the Tabasco, milk and salt and pepper to taste in a separate bowl.

3 Whisk the egg whites in a large bowl until stiff, then gently stir the egg yolk mixture into the egg whites, taking care not to over-mix.

4 Heat the oil in a large, non-stick frying pan and when hot pour in the egg mixture. Cook over a low heat for 4–6 minutes, or until lightly set. Preheat the grill.

5 Spoon the prawn mixture on top of the eggs and sprinkle with the cheese. Cook under the preheated grill for 2–3 minutes, or until set and the top is golden brown. Cut into wedges and serve immediately.

serves 4–6 (4 as a meal on its own or 6 as part of a brunch)

Fish Brunch

Ingredients

100 g/3½ oz brown rice
salt and pepper
few saffron strands
300 g/10½ oz undyed smoked haddock fillets
1 bay leaf
1 large onion
150 ml/5 fl oz milk
115 g/4 oz French beans, chopped
2 tbsp olive oil
1–2 garlic cloves, crushed
150 ml/5 fl oz fish stock
115 g/4 oz sweetcorn kernels, thawed if frozen
2 tomatoes, chopped
225 g/8 oz raw tiger prawns, peeled
1 tbsp chopped fresh coriander

1 Cook the rice in a saucepan of lightly salted boiling water with the saffron for 25 minutes, or until tender. Drain and reserve.

2 Meanwhile, rinse the haddock and put into a frying pan with the bay leaf. Cut a few slices off the onion and add to the pan. Pour over the milk and bring to the boil, then reduce the heat and simmer for 10 minutes, or until the fish is cooked. Drain and leave to cool slightly. When cool enough to handle, remove and discard the skin and any remaining bones and flake the flesh into small pieces.

3 Cook the beans in a saucepan of lightly salted boiling water for 5 minutes, drain, then plunge into cold water. Drain again and reserve.

4 Finely chop the remaining onion. Heat the oil in large frying pan over a medium heat, add the onion and garlic and cook for 5 minutes, stirring frequently. Add the rice, stock, haddock, beans, sweetcorn, tomatoes and tiger prawns. Cook, stirring occasionally, for 10 minutes, or until the prawns are cooked and have turned pink. Add salt and pepper to taste, stir in the coriander and serve.

Nutritional Fact

Brown rice still contains the hulls that are removed in processing to make white rice; these provide B vitamins and fibre, which slow down the release of the starch into the bloodstream.

Serving Analysis

- *Calories* — 476
- *Protein* — 38g
- *Carbohydrate* — 56g
- *Sugars* — 11.6g
- *Fat* — 10.4g
- *Saturates* — 0.8g
- *GI* — Low

Soups & Light Meals

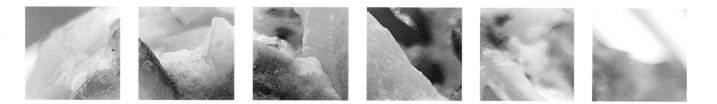

Whether you are looking for a speedy snack at lunch or suppertime or have to cater for an unexpected guest, you are sure to find something suitable and appetizing in this chapter. Most of the dishes take only a short time to prepare and cook, and if necessary can be prepared ahead of time and quickly cooked when required. Try the Chicken & Broccoli Soup, a hearty soup chock-full of chunky pieces of chicken, broccoli and sweetcorn, or the Roasted Vegetable Salad – ideal for any occasion, served warm or cold. The Home-made Hummus and Tapenade are also easy and versatile options, making elegant starters as well as everyday snacks.

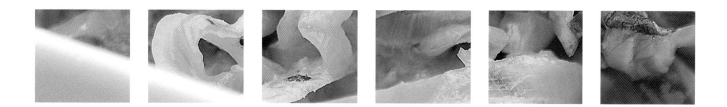

serves 4

Tomato & Bean Soup

Ingredients

1 tbsp olive oil

1 onion, chopped

2–3 garlic cloves, crushed

2 celery sticks, chopped

1 fresh red chilli, deseeded and chopped

1 tbsp tomato purée

1 litre/1³/₄ pints vegetable stock

400 g/14 oz canned chopped tomatoes

200 g/7 oz canned red kidney beans, drained and rinsed

300 g/10¹/₂ oz canned cannellini beans, drained and rinsed

salt and pepper

85 g/3 oz cooked brown rice

1–2 tbsp chopped fresh basil

freshly grated Parmesan cheese (optional), to serve

Nutritional Fact
Beans are a fantastic source of vegetable protein and provide plenty of soluble fibre and B vitamins, which both help to regulate energy production and blood-sugar control.

Serving Analysis
- Calories   194
- Protein   8.3g
- Carbohydrate   31g
- Sugars   5.8g
- Fat   4.6g
- Saturates   0.6g
- GI   Low

1 Heat the oil in a large saucepan over a medium heat, add the onion, garlic, celery and chilli and cook for 3 minutes, stirring occasionally.

2 Blend the tomato purée with the stock and add to the saucepan with the tomatoes. Bring to the boil, then reduce the heat and simmer for 10 minutes.

3 Add the beans and salt and pepper to taste and simmer for a further 10 minutes.

4 Stir in the rice and cook for a further 5 minutes, or until all the ingredients are piping hot. Serve sprinkled with the basil and with Parmesan cheese, if desired.

serves 4

Laksa

Ingredients

1 tbsp sunflower oil

2–3 garlic cloves, cut into thin slivers

1–2 fresh red Thai chillies, deseeded and sliced

2 lemon grass stalks, outer leaves removed, chopped

2.5-cm/1-inch piece fresh root ginger, grated

1. 2 litres/2 pints fish or vegetable stock

350 g/12 oz large raw prawns, peeled and deveined

115 g/4 oz shiitake mushrooms, sliced

1 large carrot, grated

55 g/2 oz dried egg noodles (optional)

1–2 tsp Thai fish sauce

1 tbsp chopped fresh coriander

1 Heat the oil in a large saucepan over a medium heat, add the garlic, chillies, lemon grass and ginger and cook for 5 minutes, stirring frequently. Add the stock and bring to the boil, then reduce the heat and simmer for 5 minutes.

2 Stir in the prawns, mushrooms and carrot. If using the egg noodles, break into small lengths, add to the saucepan and simmer for a further 5 minutes, or until the prawns have turned pink and the noodles are tender.

3 Stir in the Thai fish sauce and coriander and heat through for a further minute before serving.

Nutritional Fact
Ginger gives this dish its curative properties and also improves digestion and circulation. It is anti-inflammatory and can help to alleviate many common ailments.

Serving Analysis

- *Calories* — *157*
- *Protein* — *20g*
- *Carbohydrate* — *8.1g*
- *Sugars* — *2.1g*
- *Fat* — *5.2g*
- *Saturates* — *0.8g*
- *GI* — *Low*

serves 4

Smoky Fish & Bacon Cakes

1 Remove and discard any remaining bones from the fish fillets, lightly rinse and put into a large frying pan with the milk, onion, carrot, celery and bay leaf. Bring to a gentle boil, then reduce the heat and simmer for 8–10 minutes, or until just cooked. Remove from the heat, leave to cool, then strain off the milk and reserve. When the fish is cool enough to handle, flake the flesh and reserve.

Ingredients

280 g/10 oz undyed smoked haddock fillets, skinned

280 g/10 oz fresh haddock or cod fillets, skinned

150 ml/5 fl oz milk

1 small onion, cut into thick slices

1 carrot, cut into thick slices

1 celery stick, sliced

1 bay leaf

225 g/8 oz potatoes, peeled and cut into chunks

1 tbsp chopped fresh tarragon

1 tbsp finely grated lemon rind

salt and pepper

8 back bacon rashers

1–2 tbsp sunflower oil

freshly cooked broccoli florets and grilled pepper wedges or baked beans and fresh tomato sauce (see page 13), to serve

2 Meanwhile, cook the potatoes in a saucepan of lightly salted boiling water for 15 minutes, or until tender. Drain and mash, adding a little of the reserved milk to give a smooth but not sloppy consistency.

3 Add the fish with the tarragon, lemon rind and salt and pepper to taste and mix together. Leave to cool.

4 Shape the mixture into 4 or 8 fish cakes and wrap 1 or 2 bacon rashers around each fish cake. Cover and chill in the refrigerator until required.

5 When ready to cook, heat the oil in a frying pan over a medium heat, add the fish cakes and cook for 4–5 minutes on both sides, or until golden brown and piping hot. Drain and serve with cooked broccoli florets and grilled pepper wedges or baked beans and tomato sauce.

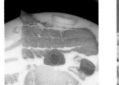

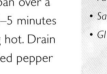

Nutritional Fact

White fish contains good levels of vitamin A, which protects the eyes, liver, heart and skin from damage from light, pollution and toxins.

Serving Analysis

* Calories   397
* Protein   41g
* Carbohydrate   14g
* Sugars   4.4g
* Fat   19g
* Saturates   5.5g
* GI   Low

serves 4–6

Chicken & Broccoli Soup

Ingredients

225 g/8 oz broccoli

salt and pepper

55 g/2 oz unsalted butter

1 onion, chopped

25 g/1 oz basmati rice

225 g/8 oz skinless, boneless chicken breast, cut into thin slivers

25 g/1 oz plain wholemeal flour

300 ml/10 fl oz milk

450 ml/16 fl oz chicken stock

55 g/2 oz sweetcorn kernels

Nutritional Fact

Broccoli is an absolute wonder food that increases liver function and also cleans out cells due to its high sulphur content.

Serving Analysis

• *Calories*	*220*
• *Protein*	*15g*
• *Carbohydrate*	*16g*
• *Sugars*	*5.8g*
• *Fat*	*11g*
• *Saturates*	*6.5g*
• *GI*	*Low*

1 Break the broccoli into small florets and cook in a saucepan of lightly salted boiling water for 3 minutes, drain, then plunge into cold water and reserve.

2 Melt the butter in a saucepan over a medium heat, add the onion, rice and chicken and cook for 5 minutes, stirring frequently.

3 Remove the saucepan from the heat and stir in the flour. Return to the heat and cook for 2 minutes, stirring constantly. Stir in the milk and then the stock. Bring to the boil, stirring constantly, then reduce the heat and simmer for 10 minutes.

4 Drain the broccoli and add to the saucepan with the sweetcorn and salt and pepper to taste. Simmer for 5 minutes, or until the rice is tender, then serve.

serves 4

Cajun Chicken Salad

Ingredients

4 skinless, boneless chicken breasts, about 140 g/5 oz each

4 tsp Cajun seasoning

2 tsp sunflower oil (optional)

1 ripe mango, peeled, stoned and cut into thick slices

200 g/7 oz mixed salad leaves

1 red onion, thinly sliced and cut in half

175 g/6 oz cooked beetroot, diced

85 g/3 oz radishes, sliced

55 g/2 oz walnut halves

4 tbsp walnut oil

1–2 tsp Dijon mustard

1 tbsp lemon juice

salt and pepper

2 tbsp sesame seeds

1 Make 3 diagonal slashes across each chicken breast. Put the chicken into a shallow dish and sprinkle all over with the Cajun seasoning. Cover and refrigerate for at least 30 minutes.

2 When ready to cook, brush a griddle pan with the sunflower oil, if using. Heat over a high heat until very hot and a few drops of water sprinkled into the pan sizzle immediately. Add the chicken and cook for 7–8 minutes on each side, or until thoroughly cooked. If still slightly pink in the centre, cook a little longer. Remove the chicken and reserve.

3 Add the mango slices to the pan and cook for 2 minutes on each side. Remove and reserve.

4 Meanwhile, arrange the salad leaves in a salad bowl and scatter over the onion, beetroot, radishes and walnut halves.

5 Put the walnut oil, mustard, lemon juice and salt and pepper to taste in a screw-top jar and shake until well blended. Pour over the salad and sprinkle with the sesame seeds.

6 Arrange the mango and the salad on a serving plate and top with the chicken breast and a few of the salad leaves.

Nutritional Fact
Beetroot helps stimulate the liver and cleans out toxins from the bowels.

Serving Analysis

• Calories	477
• Protein	38g
• Carbohydrate	23g
• Sugars	15g
• Fat	27g
• Saturates	2.9g
• GI	Low

serves 4

Creamy Leek Bake

Ingredients

55 g/2 oz unsalted butter, melted

115 g/4 oz ground almonds

55 g/2 oz toasted chopped hazelnuts

25 g/1 oz sesame seeds

85 g/3 oz mature Cheddar cheese, grated

1 tbsp virgin olive oil

350 g/12 oz leeks, thinly sliced

1 large red pepper, skinned, deseeded and cut into strips

1 orange pepper, skinned, deseeded and cut into strips

85 g/3 oz button mushrooms, sliced

250 g/9 oz crème fraîche

1 tbsp chopped fresh oregano

salt and pepper

Nutritional Fact

Oregano is a member of the mint family and a potent natural antiseptic. It also aids digestion of heavy meals by calming the gut.

Serving Analysis

- Calories   691
- Protein   20g
- Carbohydrate   21g
- Sugars   5.7g
- Fat   62g
- Saturates   22g
- GI   Low

1 Preheat the oven to 190°C/375°F/Gas Mark 5. Mix the butter, nuts, sesame seeds and half the cheese together in a bowl. Press the mixture into the base of an 850-ml/1½-pint ovenproof gratin dish. Bake in the preheated oven for 15 minutes, or until the top is golden.

2 Meanwhile, heat the oil in a large frying pan over a medium heat, add the leeks, peppers and mushrooms and cook for 5 minutes, stirring occasionally. Stir in the crème fraîche, oregano and salt and pepper to taste.

3 Remove the nut base from the oven. Spread the crème fraîche mixture over the nut base and sprinkle with the remaining cheese. Bake in the oven for 15–20 minutes, or until the cheese is golden brown and bubbling.

serves 4

Roasted Vegetable Salad

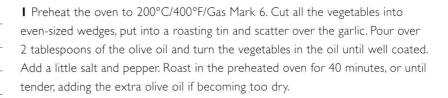

Ingredients

| 1 onion |
| 1 aubergine, about 225 g/8 oz |
| 1 red pepper, deseeded |
| 1 orange pepper, deseeded |
| 1 large courgette, about 175 g/6 oz |
| 2–4 garlic cloves |
| 2–4 tbsp olive oil |
| salt and pepper |
| 1 tbsp balsamic vinegar |
| 2 tbsp extra virgin olive oil |
| 1 tbsp shredded fresh basil |
| freshly shaved Parmesan cheese, to serve |

1 Preheat the oven to 200°C/400°F/Gas Mark 6. Cut all the vegetables into even-sized wedges, put into a roasting tin and scatter over the garlic. Pour over 2 tablespoons of the olive oil and turn the vegetables in the oil until well coated. Add a little salt and pepper. Roast in the preheated oven for 40 minutes, or until tender, adding the extra olive oil if becoming too dry.

2 Meanwhile, put the vinegar, extra virgin olive oil and salt and pepper to taste into a screw-top jar and shake until blended.

3 Once the vegetables are cooked, remove from the oven, arrange on a serving dish and pour over the dressing. Sprinkle with the basil and serve with shavings of Parmesan cheese. Serve warm or cold.

Nutritional Fact
Roasting vegetables is a tasty way to eat the recommended five portions of vegetables and fruit per day. The benefits are heightened by including vegetables of different colours.

Serving Analysis
- *Calories*   *216*
- *Protein*   *2.1g*
- *Carbohydrate*   *12g*
- *Sugars*   *6.4g*
- *Fat*   *18g*
- *Saturates*   *2.6g*
- *GI*   *Medium*

makes 450 g/1 lb

Home-made Hummus

Ingredients

400 g/14 oz canned chickpeas, drained

2 tbsp tahini paste

4–6 tbsp virgin olive oil

4–6 tbsp lemon juice

2–3 garlic cloves, crushed

1–2 tbsp hot water

salt and pepper

red and orange pepper strips, celery sticks and cucumber sticks, to serve

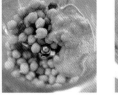 

1 Put all the ingredients (except the crudités) into a food processor and process to form a fairly smooth paste. Using the pulse button, slowly blend in the hot water to give a dipping consistency. Add salt and pepper to taste.

2 Spoon into a small serving dish, cover and store in the refrigerator until required. Serve with the vegetable crudités.

Nutritional Fact

The high raw garlic content of these dips provides a high level of the compound allicin, which has antibacterial and heart protecting properties.

Analysis for Recipe

HUMMUS

- *Calories*   1326
- *Protein*   25.6g
- *Carbohydrate*   105g
- *Sugars*   20g
- *Fat*   90g
- *Saturates*   12.7g
- *GI*   Low

Analysis for Recipe

TAPENADE

- *Calories*   651
- *Protein*   17g
- *Carbohydrate*   20g
- *Sugars*   0.1g
- *Fat*   58g
- *Saturates*   3.3g
- *GI*   Low

makes 500 g/1 lb 2 oz

Home-made Tapenade

Ingredients

225 g/8 oz pitted black olives

40 g/1 1/2 oz capers, drained and rinsed if salty

2 garlic cloves, crushed

1 tbsp chopped fresh thyme

1 tsp Dijon mustard

55 g/2 oz canned anchovies, rinsed and patted dry

100–125 ml/3 1/2–4 fl oz virgin olive oil

1–2 tbsp brandy or hot water

pepper

2 tsp chopped fresh parsley, to garnish

red and orange pepper strips, celery sticks and cucumber sticks, to serve

1 Put the olives, capers, garlic, thyme, mustard and anchovies with their oil into a food processor and process until smooth. Using the pulse button, slowly blend in the oil until a thick purée is formed. Stir in the brandy or water and add pepper to taste.

2 Spoon into a small serving dish, cover and store in the refrigerator until required. Serve, scattered with parsley, with the vegetable crudités.

Seafood, Meat & Poultry

Here is a range of delicious main dishes that will satisfy the heartiest appetite, leaving you and your guests feeling full and energized. Choose from tender, succulent roast lamb served with a clean-tasting green salsa and sweet potato mash, garlic-scented monkfish cooked on a bed of roasted vegetables or the comforting Beef & Bean Hot Pot, thickened with nutritious pearl barley. Alternatively, sample turkey steaks marinated for added flavour and tenderness before being griddled and served with a cannellini bean purée. Whichever dish you choose, it is sure to be a winner with both family and friends.

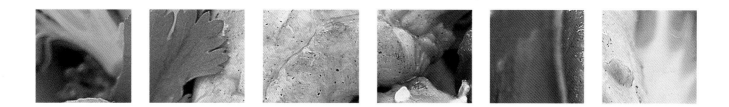

serves 4

Roasted Monkfish

Ingredients

675 g/1 lb 8 oz monkfish tail, skinned
4–5 large garlic cloves, peeled
salt and pepper
3 tbsp olive oil
1 onion, cut into wedges
1 small aubergine, about 300 g/10^{1}/$_{2}$ oz, cut into chunks
1 red pepper, deseeded, cut into wedges
1 yellow pepper, deseeded, cut into wedges
1 large courgette, about 225 g/8 oz, cut into wedges
1 tbsp shredded fresh basil

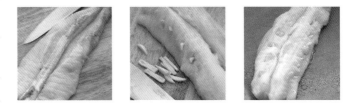

Nutritional Fact

Cooking in olive oil is the safest way to avoid damaged fats that can harm the body; olive oil is monounsaturated, which makes it remain stable when heated to moderate temperatures.

Serving Analysis

- Calories   289
- Protein   27g
- Carbohydrate   14g
- Sugars   7.2g
- Fat   13.5g
- Saturates   2.2g
- GI   Low

1 Preheat the oven to 200°C/400°F/Gas Mark 6. Remove the central bone from the fish if not already removed and make small slits down each fillet. Cut 2 of the garlic cloves into thin slivers and insert into the fish. Place the fish on a sheet of greaseproof paper, season with salt and pepper to taste and drizzle over 1 tablespoon of the oil. Bring the top edges together. Form into a pleat and fold over, then fold the ends underneath, completely encasing the fish. Reserve.

2 Put the remaining garlic cloves and all the vegetables into a roasting tin and sprinkle with the remaining oil, turning the vegetables so that they are well coated in the oil.

3 Roast in the preheated oven for 20 minutes, turning occasionally. Put the fish parcel on top of the vegetables and cook for a further 15–20 minutes, or until the vegetables are tender and the fish is cooked.

4 Remove from the oven and open up the parcel. Cut the monkfish into thick slices. Arrange the vegetables on warmed serving plates, top with the fish slices and sprinkle with the basil. Serve immediately.

serves 4

Braised Seafood with Fennel

Ingredients

550 g/1 lb 4 oz assorted seafood such as salmon, cod, swordfish, large raw tiger prawns and squid, cleaned

2 tbsp olive oil

1 onion, cut into wedges

1 fennel bulb, cut into thin wedges

400 g/14 oz canned chopped tomatoes

150 ml/5 fl oz orange juice

1 tbsp finely grated orange rind

55 g/2 oz pitted black olives

salt and pepper

1 tbsp chopped fresh flat-leaved parsley

fresh salad, such as baby spinach leaves, watercress, chicory and orange segments, to serve

Nutritional Fact

Fennel contains volatile oils which help all aspects of digestion as they inhibit spasms in all smooth muscle, including the digestive tract, so reducing flatulence and bloating.

Serving Analysis

• Calories	476
• Protein	12g
• Carbohydrate	21g
• Sugars	7.8g
• Fat	39g
• Saturates	5.3g
• GI	Low

1 Prepare the seafood by removing and discarding any skin and bones from the fish and cutting into bite-sized pieces. Peel and devein the prawns. Cut the squid into thin slices or rings. Rinse all the fish and pat dry with kitchen paper.

2 Heat the oil in a large frying pan over a medium heat, add the onion and fennel and cook, stirring occasionally, for 10 minutes, or until beginning to soften. Add the tomatoes and orange juice and rind and bring to the boil, then reduce the heat and simmer for 6–8 minutes.

3 Add the fish but not the prawns or squid and simmer for a further 5 minutes before adding the remaining seafood and the olives. Cook for a further 4–5 minutes, or until all the seafood is cooked and tender. Season to taste with salt and pepper, sprinkle with the parsley and serve with a fresh salad.

Nutritional Fact

The garlic and coriander help to stimulate digestion and encourage enzymes that help to break down the rich protein of the lamb.

Serving Analysis

• Calories	832
• Protein	43g
• Carbohydrate	13g
• Sugars	5.4g
• Fat	68g
• Saturates	22g
• GI	Low

serves 4

Pan-fried Lamb Noisettes

1 First make the pesto. If using fresh or frozen broad beans, cook in a saucepan of lightly salted boiling water for 10 minutes, or until tender. Drain and put into a food processor with the garlic and coriander. Using the pulse button, finely chop.

2 With the motor running, slowly pour in the extra virgin olive oil, ensuring that it is well blended. When all the oil has been incorporated, scrape the pesto into a bowl and add salt and pepper to taste and the Parmesan cheese. Spoon into a serving bowl, cover and chill in the refrigerator until required.

3 Meanwhile, arrange the aubergine slices on a large baking sheet and sprinkle with the olive oil, reserving 1 teaspoon, then scatter over the garlic and chilli. Leave for at least 30 minutes.

4 Preheat the grill to medium and cover the grill rack with foil. Arrange a single layer of aubergine slices on the grill rack and cook under the preheated grill for 3–5 minutes, turning once, until tender and beginning to crisp. Remove and keep warm while cooking the remaining slices and lamb.

5 Meanwhile, preheat a non-stick frying pan over a medium heat. Season the lamb noisettes, add to the pan and brown on all sides, then cook for 6–8 minutes on each side, or until cooked to your personal preference.

6 Arrange 4 aubergine slices on each serving plate, top with the lamb and serve, garnished with coriander sprigs, with a spoonful of pesto.

Ingredients

1 large aubergine, cut into 16 slices

3 tbsp olive oil

3 large garlic cloves, crushed

1 fresh red jalapeño chilli, deseeded and finely chopped

8 lamb noisettes

salt and pepper

fresh coriander sprigs, to garnish

For the pesto

115 g/4 oz shelled fresh, frozen or canned broad beans

salt and pepper

1 large garlic clove, crushed

1 tbsp chopped fresh coriander

100 ml/3 1/2 fl oz extra virgin olive oil

1 1/2 tbsp freshly grated Parmesan cheese

serves 4

Crusted Rack of Lamb

1 Preheat the oven to 190°C/375°F/Gas Mark 5. Wipe the lamb racks with kitchen paper and wrap the ends of the bones with foil.

2 Mix the breadcrumbs, garlic, herbs, lemon rind and salt and pepper to taste together in a bowl and bind with the egg. Press on to the skinned side of the lamb. Stand the racks in a roasting tin and roast in the preheated oven for 40–50 minutes, or until cooked to your personal preference.

3 Remove from the oven, remove and discard the foil from the bones and cover with a sheet of foil. Leave to rest for 5 minutes.

4 Meanwhile, mix all the salsa ingredients together in a small serving bowl, cover and reserve until required.

5 Cook the sweet potatoes in a saucepan of lightly salted boiling water for 15–20 minutes, or until tender when pierced with a fork. Drain, mash, then beat in the milk and mint until smooth.

6 Serve the lamb racks with the salsa and mash, accompanied by a lightly cooked green vegetable, such as broccoli.

Ingredients

2 racks of lamb, about 6–8 chops each, skin removed, trimmed of any excess fat

40 g/1¹/₂ oz fresh wholemeal breadcrumbs

2–3 garlic cloves, crushed

2 tbsp chopped fresh parsley

1 tbsp chopped fresh mint

1 tbsp finely grated lemon rind

salt and pepper

1 egg

lightly cooked green vegetable, such as broccoli, to serve

For the salsa

1 small green dessert apple, washed, cored and finely diced

2 tomatoes, deseeded and finely diced

3 spring onions, finely chopped

1 tbsp chopped fresh mint

For the mash

450 g/1 lb sweet potatoes, peeled and chopped

2 tbsp milk

1 tbsp chopped fresh mint

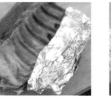

Nutritional Fact

Parsley and mint help the digestive process and sweet potatoes are a rich source of beta-carotene, which gives them their bright colour and protects the body from UV damage from the sun.

Serving Analysis

- *Calories*   *624*
- *Protein*   *42g*
- *Carbohydrate*   *43g*
- *Sugars*   *19g*
- *Fat*   *31g*
- *Saturates*   *14g*
- *GI*   *Low*

serves 4

Beef & Bean Hot Pot

Ingredients

2 tbsp olive oil
8 shallots, peeled
2 celery sticks, chopped
175 g/6 oz carrots, cut into chunks
550 g/1 lb 4 oz braising steak, trimmed of any visible fat and diced
1 tbsp plain wholemeal flour
1 tbsp tomato purée
600 ml/1 pint beef stock
55 g/2 oz pearl barley, rinsed
salt and pepper
550 g/1 lb 4 oz sweet potatoes, peeled and sliced
1 tbsp chopped fresh parsley

Nutritional Fact

Celery is high in the chemical apigenin, which expands blood vessels and helps to prevent high blood pressure.

Serving Analysis

- Calories   566
- Protein   48g
- Carbohydrate   52g
- Sugars   11g
- Fat   18g
- Saturates   3.7g
- GI   Low

1 Preheat the oven to 180°C/350°F/Gas Mark 4. Heat half the oil in a large saucepan over a medium heat, add the shallots, celery and carrots and cook for 2 minutes, stirring frequently. Add the steak and cook, stirring constantly, for 2–3 minutes, or until the meat is sealed on all sides.

2 Sprinkle in the flour and cook, stirring constantly, for 2 minutes. Blend the tomato purée with a little of the stock and stir into the saucepan, then stir in the remaining stock and the pearl barley. Bring to the boil, stirring constantly, then reduce the heat and simmer for 5 minutes. Season to taste with salt and pepper and transfer to an ovenproof casserole dish.

3 Arrange the sweet potato slices on top and brush with the remaining oil. Bake in the preheated oven for 2–2$^{1}/_{2}$ hours, or until the meat and vegetables are tender. Remove the lid for the last 20 minutes of the cooking time to crisp the top. Sprinkle with the parsley before serving.

serves 4

Chicken with Pak Choi

Ingredients

175 g/6 oz broccoli
1 tbsp groundnut oil
2.5-cm/1-inch piece fresh root ginger, finely grated
1 fresh red Thai chilli, deseeded and chopped
2 garlic cloves, crushed
1 red onion, cut into wedges
450 g/1 lb skinless, boneless chicken breast, cut into thin strips
175 g/6 oz pak choi, shredded
115 g/4 oz baby corn, halved
1 tbsp light soy sauce
1 tbsp Thai fish sauce
1 tbsp chopped fresh coriander
1 tbsp toasted sesame seeds

1 Break the broccoli into small florets and cook in a saucepan of lightly salted boiling water for 3 minutes. Drain and reserve.

2 Heat a wok over a high heat until almost smoking, add the oil and then add the ginger, chilli and garlic. Stir-fry for 1 minute. Add the onion and chicken and stir-fry for a further 3–4 minutes, or until the chicken is sealed on all sides.

3 Add the remaining vegetables, including the broccoli, and stir-fry for 3–4 minutes, or until tender.

4 Add the soy and Thai fish sauces and stir-fry for a further 1–2 minutes, then serve immediately sprinkled with the coriander and sesame seeds.

Nutritional Fact

Chicken is a source of complete protein, which, like all meats, means that it provides all the amino acids that help us to build body structures like skin, bones and teeth. It has less saturated fat than red meat.

Serving Analysis

• Calories	233
• Protein	31g
• Carbohydrate	14g
• Sugars	4.8g
• Fat	6.6g
• Saturates	2.2g
• GI	Low

serves 4

Chicken Tagine

Ingredients

1 tbsp olive oil

1 onion, cut into small wedges

2–4 garlic cloves, sliced

450 g/1 lb skinless, boneless chicken breast, diced

1 tsp ground cumin

2 cinnamon sticks, lightly bruised

1 tbsp plain wholemeal flour

225 g/8 oz aubergine, diced

1 red pepper, deseeded and chopped

85 g/3 oz button mushrooms, sliced

1 tbsp tomato purée

600 ml/1 pint chicken stock

280 g/10 oz canned chickpeas, drained and rinsed

55 g/2 oz no-soak dried apricots, chopped

salt and pepper

1 tbsp chopped fresh coriander

1 Heat the oil in a large saucepan over a medium heat, add the onion and garlic and cook for 3 minutes, stirring frequently. Add the chicken and cook, stirring constantly, for a further 5 minutes, or until sealed on all sides. Add the cumin and cinnamon sticks to the saucepan halfway through sealing the chicken.

2 Sprinkle in the flour and cook, stirring constantly, for 2 minutes.

3 Add the aubergine, red pepper and mushrooms and cook for a further 2 minutes, stirring constantly.

4 Blend the tomato purée with the stock, stir into the saucepan and bring to the boil. Reduce the heat and add the chickpeas and apricots. Cover and simmer for 15–20 minutes, or until the chicken is tender.

5 Season with salt and pepper to taste and serve immediately, sprinkled with coriander.

Nutritional Fact

Chickpeas provide protein as well as calcium and iron and, like other pulses, have been shown to reduce cholesterol and glucose in the blood and are therefore good for the heart.

Serving Analysis

- Calories   313
- Protein   32g
- Carbohydrate   32g
- Sugars   13.5g
- Fat   6.2g
- Saturates   0.5g
- GI   Low

serves 4

Turkey Steaks with Bean Purée

Ingredients

4 turkey breast fillet steaks, about 140 g/5 oz each

1 tbsp redcurrant jelly

2 tbsp red wine vinegar

1 tbsp orange juice

fresh redcurrants, to garnish (optional)

freshly cooked French beans, tossed in butter, with 225 g/8 oz halved cherry tomatoes and 4 chopped spring onions, to serve

For the bean purée

2 tbsp olive oil

500 g/1 lb 2 oz canned cannellini beans, drained, rinsed and roughly mashed

2–3 garlic cloves, crushed

1 tbsp chopped fresh mint

Nutritional Fact

Turkey is a good source of the amino acid or protein building block tryptophan, which the body makes into the neurotransmitter serotonin; this helps us sleep and feel content.

Serving Analysis

- *Calories* — *400*
- *Protein* — *36g*
- *Carbohydrate* — *23g*
- *Sugars* — *3.7g*
- *Fat* — *17g*
- *Saturates* — *2.7g*
- *GI* — *Low*

1 Wipe the turkey steaks with kitchen paper and put into a large, shallow dish. Heat the redcurrant jelly with the vinegar and orange juice in a small saucepan over a low heat and stir until smooth. Pour over the turkey, cover and leave for at least 30 minutes.

2 When ready to cook, heat a griddle pan over a high heat until almost smoking. Add the turkey and cook for 5–6 minutes on each side, or until thoroughly cooked.

3 Meanwhile, mix all the ingredients for the bean purée together in a bowl, transfer to a non-stick saucepan over a low heat and heat through, stirring frequently, for 6–7 minutes, or until piping hot. Alternatively, transfer the mixture to a microwaveproof container, cover with clingfilm and heat in a 1,000-watt microwave oven for 3–4 minutes. Remove and leave to stand for 2 minutes. Remove and discard the clingfilm and stir well.

4 Serve the turkey steaks on the bean purée with freshly cooked French beans, tossed in butter, with cherry tomatoes and spring onions, garnished with redcurrants, if desired.

Vegetarian

These recipes are not just for vegetarians – they will appeal to all who enjoy exciting taste and texture combinations. The Dolcelatte & Vegetable Cheesecake offers a wonderful contrast of a crispy, nutty base and a creamy vegetable filling, while the Vegetable Biryani is bursting with aromatic flavours. Among other tasty fresh vegetables, such as field mushrooms and asparagus, broccoli features quite heavily, and for good reason. Not only is it flavourful and versatile, it also offers excellent health-promoting properties. Crammed full of the antioxidant vitamins beta-carotene and vitamin C, which are believed to help protect against cancer, it is also high in fibre with a low Glycaemic Index.

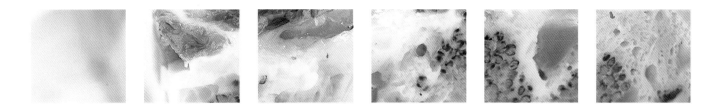

serves 4–6

Three Bean Salad

Ingredients

175 g/6 oz mixed salad leaves, such as spinach, rocket and frisée

1 red onion

85 g/3 oz radishes

175 g/6 oz cherry tomatoes

115 g/4 oz cooked beetroot

280 g/10 oz canned cannellini beans, drained and rinsed

200 g/7 oz canned red kidney beans, drained and rinsed

300 g/10$^{1}/_{2}$ oz canned flageolet beans, drained and rinsed

40 g/1$^{1}/_{2}$ oz dried cranberries

55 g/2 oz roasted cashew nuts

225 g/8 oz feta cheese (drained weight), crumbled

For the dressing

4 tbsp extra virgin olive oil

1 tsp Dijon mustard

2 tbsp lemon juice

1 tbsp chopped fresh coriander

salt and pepper

1 Arrange the salad leaves in a salad bowl and reserve.

2 Thinly slice the onion, then cut in half to form half moons and put into a bowl.

3 Thinly slice the radishes, cut the tomatoes in half and peel the beetroot if necessary and dice. Add to the onion with the remaining ingredients, except the nuts and cheese.

4 Put all the ingredients for the dressing into a screw-top jar and shake until blended. Pour over the bean mixture, toss lightly, then spoon on top of the salad leaves.

5 Scatter over the nuts and cheese and serve immediately.

Nutritional Fact

Feta cheese made from goat's milk contains less of the milk sugar lactose than cheese made from cow's milk; this gives it its slightly bitter taste and makes it easier to digest.

Serving Analysis

• Calories	455
• Protein	17g
• Carbohydrate	37g
• Sugars	9.3g
• Fat	27g
• Saturates	9.5g
• GI	Low

serves 6

Dolcelatte & Vegetable Cheesecake

Ingredients

For the base

55 g/2 oz ground almonds

55 g/2 oz fresh wholemeal breadcrumbs

55 g/2 oz finely chopped toasted hazelnuts

55 g/2 oz freshly grated Parmesan cheese

55 g/2 oz unsalted butter, melted

For the filling

10 g/¼ oz sun-dried tomatoes

115 g/4 oz baby asparagus spears

115 g/4 oz broccoli

salt and pepper

1 red pepper, skinned, deseeded and cut into thin strips

140 g/5 oz dolcelatte cheese

450 g/1 lb mascarpone cheese

3 eggs

1 Preheat the oven to 180°C/350°F/Gas Mark 4. Mix the almonds, breadcrumbs, hazelnuts and Parmesan cheese together in a bowl. Stir the butter into the nut mixture, mix well, then press into the base of a 20-cm/8-inch springform tin. Bake in the preheated oven for 15 minutes, then remove from the oven and reserve.

2 Meanwhile, put the tomatoes into a heatproof bowl and cover with almost boiling water. Leave for 20 minutes, then drain and chop.

3 Trim the asparagus and, if thick, cut in half. Cut the broccoli into long, thin spears, including the stalk. Cook both together in a saucepan of lightly salted boiling water for 3 minutes, then drain, plunge into cold water and leave to cool. Drain again.

4 Arrange the vegetables and red pepper over the nut base and crumble over half the dolcelatte cheese.

5 Cream the mascarpone cheese in a bowl until soft, then gradually beat in the eggs. Continue beating until smooth. Pour over the vegetables and crumble the remaining dolcelatte cheese over the top.

6 Put the tin on a baking tray and bake in the preheated oven for 35–40 minutes, or until set.

7 Remove from the oven, release the tin and remove the cheesecake.

Nutritional Fact
Using ground nuts instead of a grain for bases and other baking helps to reduce the carbohydrate content and slow down the release of sugars into the bloodstream.

Serving Analysis
- *Calories*   727
- *Protein*   23.2g
- *Carbohydrate*   16.3g
- *Sugars*   6.7g
- *Fat*   64.7g
- *Saturates*   8g
- *GI*   Low

serves 6–8

Nutty Stilton Roast

1 Preheat the oven to 180°C/350°F/Gas Mark 4. Lightly oil a 900-g/2-lb loaf tin.

2 Finely chop one of the onions. Heat 1 tablespoon of the oil in a frying pan over a medium heat, add the chopped onion, 1–2 of the garlic cloves and the celery and cook for 5 minutes, stirring occasionally.

3 Remove from the pan, drain through a sieve or colander and transfer to a food processor with the nuts, breadcrumbs, half the cheese and the basil. Using the pulse button, blend the ingredients together, then slowly blend in the egg to form a stiff mixture. Season to taste with salt and pepper.

4 Cut the remaining onion into thin wedges. Heat the remaining oil in a frying pan over a medium heat, add the onion, remaining garlic, red pepper and courgette and cook for 5 minutes, stirring frequently. Remove from the pan, add salt and pepper to taste and drain through a sieve or colander.

5 Place half the nut mixture in the prepared tin and smooth the surface. Arrange the onion and pepper mixture on top and crumble over the remaining cheese. Top with the remaining nut mixture and press down firmly. Cover with foil.

Nutritional Fact
Chestnuts are virtually fat free and higher in complex carbohydrates than other nuts; in fact nutritionally they are similar to brown rice.

Serving Analysis
- *Calories*   462
- *Protein*   17g
- *Carbohydrate*   33g
- *Sugars*   7.5g
- *Fat*   29.5g
- *Saturates*   9.5g
- *GI*   Low

6 Bake in the preheated oven for 45 minutes. Remove the foil and bake for a further 25–35 minutes, or until cooked and firm to the touch.

7 Remove from the oven and leave to cool for 5 minutes before inverting on to a warmed serving platter. Serve with a little of the tomato sauce drizzled over the top, garnished with basil sprigs and cherry tomatoes, accompanied by a green salad or vegetables.

Ingredients

2 tbsp virgin olive oil, plus extra for oiling

2 onions

3–5 garlic cloves, crushed

2 celery stalks, finely sliced

175 g/6 oz cooked and peeled chestnuts

175 g/6 oz mixed chopped nuts

55 g/2 oz ground almonds

55 g/2 oz fresh wholemeal breadcrumbs

225 g/8 oz Stilton cheese, crumbled

1 tbsp chopped fresh basil, plus extra sprigs to garnish

1 egg, beaten

salt and pepper

1 red pepper, skinned, deseeded and cut into thin wedges

1 courgette, about 115 g/4 oz, cut into wedges

cherry tomatoes, to garnish

To serve

quick tomato sauce (see page 13)

green salad or lightly cooked vegetables

serves 4

Baked Field Mushrooms

Ingredients

4 large field mushrooms

200 g/7 oz canned red kidney beans, drained and rinsed

4 spring onions

1 fresh red jalapeño chilli, deseeded and finely chopped

1 tbsp finely grated lemon rind

1 tbsp chopped fresh flat-leaved parsley, plus extra sprigs to garnish

salt and pepper

85 g/3 oz courgette, coarsely grated

85 g/3 oz carrots, coarsely grated

55 g/2 oz pine kernels, toasted

40 g/1 1/2 oz raisins

300 ml/10 fl oz vegetable stock

For the sauce

150 ml/5 fl oz Greek-style yogurt

1 tbsp chopped fresh parsley, plus extra to garnish

1 tbsp grated lemon rind

salt and pepper

asparagus and pepper stir-fry, to serve (optional)

Nutritional Fact

Many studies have been done on mushrooms and their abilities to enhance the immune system and feed the good bacteria in the gut; they are also high in minerals and protein.

Serving Analysis

• Calories	214
• Protein	10g
• Carbohydrate	27g
• Sugars	13.3g
• Fat	8.8g
• Saturates	2g
• GI	Low

1 Preheat the oven to 180°C/350°F/Gas Mark 4. Peel the mushrooms and carefully remove the stalks. Trim and rinse the stalks.

2 Put the beans, mushroom stalks, spring onions, chilli, lemon rind, parsley and salt and pepper to taste into a food processor and process for 2 minutes.

3 Scrape the mixture into a bowl and add the courgette, carrots, pine kernels and raisins. Mix well and use to stuff the mushroom cups.

4 Arrange the stuffed mushrooms in an ovenproof dish, pour round the stock and cover with foil. Bake in the preheated oven for 30 minutes, removing the foil for the last 10 minutes of the cooking time.

5 Meanwhile, to make the sauce, blend all the ingredients together in a small serving dish.

6 Serve the mushrooms hot with the sauce, garnished with parsley sprigs and accompanied by an asparagus and pepper stir-fry, if desired.

serves 6

Vegetable Pot

Ingredients

2 tbsp olive oil

8 baby onions, peeled

2 celery stalks, sliced

225 g/8 oz carrots, thickly sliced

225 g/8 oz turnips, diced

55 g/2 oz pearl barley, rinsed

700–850 ml/1 1/4–1 1/2 pints vegetable stock

salt and pepper

350 g/12 oz diced Quorn®

85 g/3 oz partially thawed frozen peas

1 tbsp chopped fresh parsley, to garnish

Nutritional Fact

Peas are actually a legume or bean, not a vegetable, and as such contain the chemical genistein, which studies have shown helps to guard against cancer.

Serving Analysis

- *Calories*   334
- *Protein*   50g
- *Carbohydrate*   26g
- *Sugars*   8.2g
- *Fat*   7g
- *Saturates*   0.3g
- *GI*   Medium

1 Preheat the oven to 180°C/350°F/Gas Mark 4. Heat half the oil in a large saucepan or flameproof casserole dish over a medium heat, add the onions, celery, carrots and turnips and cook for 10 minutes, stirring frequently. Add the pearl barley and cook for 1 minute, stirring occasionally, then pour in the stock and bring to the boil.

2 If necessary, transfer to an ovenproof casserole dish. Season to taste with salt and pepper and cover. Cook in the preheated oven for 1–1 1/4 hours.

3 Meanwhile, heat the remaining oil in a frying pan over a medium heat, add the Quorn® and cook, stirring frequently, for 5–8 minutes, or until golden.

4 Add the Quorn® to the casserole with the peas and cook for a further 10–20 minutes, or until the vegetables are tender. Taste and adjust the seasoning and serve sprinkled with parsley.

serves 4

Vegetable Biryani

Ingredients

2 tbsp vegetable oil

3 whole cloves

3 cardamom pods, cracked

1 onion, chopped

115 g/4 oz carrots, chopped

2–3 garlic cloves, crushed

1–2 fresh red chillies, deseeded and chopped

2.5-cm/1-inch piece fresh root ginger, grated

115 g/4 oz cauliflower, broken into small florets

175 g/6 oz broccoli, broken into small florets

115 g/4 oz French beans, chopped

400 g/14 oz canned chopped tomatoes

150 ml/5 fl oz vegetable stock

salt and pepper

115 g/4 oz okra, sliced

1 tbsp chopped fresh coriander, plus extra sprigs to garnish

115 g/4 oz brown basmati rice

few saffron strands (optional)

zested lime rind, to garnish

1 Heat the oil in a large saucepan over a low heat, add the spices, onion, carrots, garlic, chillies and ginger and cook, stirring frequently, for 5 minutes.

2 Add all the vegetables, except the okra, and cook, stirring frequently, for 5 minutes. Stir in the tomatoes, stock and salt and pepper to taste and bring to the boil. Reduce the heat, cover and simmer for 10 minutes.

3 Add the okra and cook for a further 8–10 minutes, or until the vegetables are tender. Stir in the coriander. Strain off any excess liquid and keep warm.

4 Meanwhile, cook the rice with the saffron in a saucepan of lightly salted boiling water for 25 minutes, or until tender. Drain and keep warm.

5 Layer the vegetables and cooked rice in a deep dish or pudding basin, packing the layers down firmly. Leave for about 5 minutes, then invert on to a warmed serving dish and serve, garnished with zested lime rind and coriander sprigs, with the reserved liquid.

Nutritional Fact

Cauliflower is a great source of vitamin B_6, which is needed for energy production, blood-sugar balance, correct hormone balance and good mental health and mood.

Serving Analysis

- Calories — 346
- Protein — 12.5g
- Carbohydrate — 59g
- Sugars — 14.5g
- Fat — 8.9g
- Saturates — 1.1g
- GI — Medium

serves 4

Baby Corn with Dal

Ingredients

225 g/8 oz red split lentils

2 tbsp vegetable oil

1 tsp cumin seeds

1 tsp ground coriander

$^1/_2$ tsp asafoetida

1 fresh red chilli, deseeded and finely chopped

115 g/4 oz French beans, chopped, blanched and drained

1 green pepper, deseeded and chopped

115 g/4 oz baby corn, diagonally sliced

150 ml/5 fl oz vegetable stock

2 tomatoes, deseeded and chopped

1 tbsp chopped fresh coriander

1 tbsp poppy seeds

Nutritional Fact
Cumin contains 11 chemicals with antibacterial action, which means that it helps to ward off infection and also promotes good body odour.

Serving Analysis
- *Calories*   *418*
- *Protein*   *22g*
- *Carbohydrate*   *62g*
- *Sugars*   *9.6g*
- *Fat*   *10.3g*
- *Saturates*   *1.4g*
- *GI*   *Low*

1 Rinse the lentils 2–3 times in cold water. Put into a large saucepan and cover with cold water. Bring to the boil, then reduce the heat and simmer for 15–20 minutes, or until tender. Drain, return to the saucepan and keep warm.

2 Meanwhile, heat the oil in a separate saucepan over a low heat, add the spices and chilli and cook for 2 minutes, stirring constantly. Add the beans, green pepper and baby corn and cook for 2 minutes, stirring constantly.

3 Stir in the stock and bring to the boil, then reduce the heat and simmer for 5 minutes, or until the vegetables are just tender.

4 Stir the vegetables and their liquid into the cooked lentils with the tomatoes and heat through for 5–8 minutes, or until piping hot.

5 Serve immediately sprinkled with the fresh coriander and poppy seeds.

serves 2–4 (2 as a light supper or 4 as part of a buffet)

Broccoli & Sesame Frittata

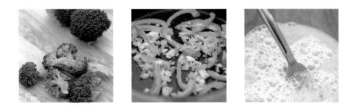

1 Cook the broccoli in a saucepan of lightly salted boiling water for 4 minutes. Add the asparagus after 2 minutes. Drain, then plunge into cold water. Drain again and reserve.

2 Heat the oil in a large frying pan over a low heat, add the onion, garlic and orange pepper and cook, stirring frequently, for 8 minutes, or until the vegetables have softened.

3 Beat the eggs with the water and salt and pepper to taste in a medium-size bowl. Pour into the pan, add the broccoli and asparagus and stir gently. Cook over a medium heat for 3–4 minutes, drawing the mixture from the edges of the pan into the centre, allowing the uncooked egg to flow to the edges of the pan. Preheat the grill.

4 Sprinkle the top of the frittata with the sesame seeds and cheese and cook under the preheated grill for 3–5 minutes, or until golden and set. Sprinkle with the spring onions, cut into wedges and serve. Serve either warm or cold.

Nutritional Fact
Sesame seeds are one of the richest sources of phytosterols, plant chemicals that can be absorbed into the bloodstream and remove the cholesterol that has built up there.

Serving Analysis

- *Calories*   *415*
- *Protein*   *26g*
- *Carbohydrate*   *19g*
- *Sugars*   *10g*
- *Fat*   *27g*
- *Saturates*   *6.5g*
- *GI*   *Low*

Ingredients

175 g/6 oz broccoli, broken into small florets
salt and pepper
85 g/3 oz asparagus spears, diagonally sliced
1 tbsp virgin olive oil
1 onion, cut into small wedges
2–4 garlic cloves, finely chopped
1 large orange pepper, deseeded and chopped
4 eggs
3 tbsp cold water
25 g/1 oz sesame seeds
15 g/½ oz freshly grated Parmesan cheese
3 spring onions, finely sliced

Desserts & Baking

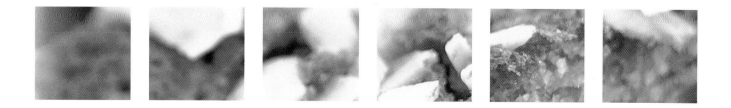

Everyone needs a treat or two occasionally, so when you are looking for one, turn immediately to this chapter. These desserts and sweet snacks are sure to tempt and delight but you can enjoy them safe in the knowledge that they are not heavily laden with undesirable sugar-rich carbohydrates.

Try the colourful Raspberry Ripple Ice Cream, which is really easy to make, or the moist Carrot Bars, ideal for lunch boxes or as an occasional afternoon-tea treat. For special occasions, everyone will be impressed by the elegant and incredibly fruity Apple & Elderflower Dessert and suitably fooled by the sumptuous Cheat's Crème Brûlée!

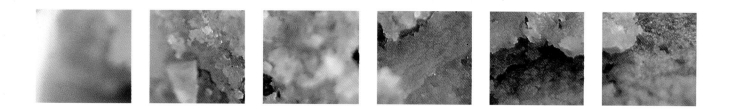

serves 6

Raspberry Ripple Ice Cream

Ingredients

85 g/3 oz fresh or frozen raspberries, thawed if frozen, plus extra to serve

2 tbsp water

2 eggs

1 tbsp caster sugar

300 ml/10 fl oz milk, warmed

1 tsp vanilla extract

300 ml/10 fl oz double cream

Nutritional Fact

Raspberries are known as a good remedy for diarrhoea. When eaten with their seeds intact, they provide many important enzymes and nutrients that we need for energy production.

Serving Analysis

- Calories   239
- Protein   4.9g
- Carbohydrate   8g
- Sugars   6.9g
- Fat   21g
- Saturates   12.6g
- GI   Low

1 Turn the freezer to rapid. Put the raspberries into a saucepan with the water and bring to the boil, then reduce the heat and simmer gently for 5 minutes. Remove from the heat and leave to cool for 30 minutes.

2 Transfer to a food processor or blender and process to a purée, then rub through a nylon sieve to remove the pips. Reserve.

3 Beat the eggs in a bowl. Stir the sugar into the warmed milk, then slowly pour on to the eggs, beating constantly. Strain into a clean saucepan and cook over a low heat, stirring constantly, for 8–10 minutes, or until the custard thickens and coats the back of a wooden spoon. Add the vanilla extract, remove from the heat and leave to cool.

4 Half-whip the cream in a large bowl, then slowly stir in the cooled custard. Pour into a freezerproof container and freeze for 1 1/2 hours, or until beginning to set around the outside. Remove from the freezer and stir the mixture, breaking up any ice crystals.

5 Return the mixture to the freezer and freeze for a further hour, then remove from the freezer and gently stir in the raspberry purée to give a rippled effect. Return to the freezer for a further hour or until frozen. Serve in scoops with extra fresh raspberries.

serves 4–6

Cheat's Crème Brûlée

Ingredients

225–300 g/8–10½ oz mixed soft fruits, such as blueberries and stoned fresh cherries

1½–2 tbsp Cointreau or orange flower water

250 g/9 oz mascarpone cheese

200 ml/7 fl oz crème fraîche

2–3 tbsp dark muscovado sugar

1 Prepare the fruit, if necessary, and lightly rinse, then place in the bases of 4–6 x 150-ml/5-fl oz ramekin dishes. Sprinkle the fruit with the Cointreau or orange flower water.

2 Cream the cheese in a bowl until soft, then gradually beat in the crème fraîche.

3 Spoon the cheese mixture over the fruit, smoothing the surface and ensuring that the tops are level. Chill in the refrigerator for at least 2 hours.

4 Sprinkle the tops with the sugar. Using a chef's blow torch, grill the tops until caramelized (about 2–3 minutes). Alternatively, cook under a preheated grill, turning the dishes, for 3–4 minutes, or until the tops are lightly caramelized all over.

5 Serve immediately or chill in the refrigerator for 15–20 minutes before serving.

Nutritional Fact
The blue pigment in blueberries is a type of anthocyadin and is a powerful liver protector; like cranberries they also help prevent urinary infections.

Serving Analysis
- *Calories*   356
- *Protein*   4.4g
- *Carbohydrate*   18g
- *Sugars*   16g
- *Fat*   30g
- *Saturates*   21.6g
- *GI*   Medium

makes 12 cups

Apricot & Yogurt Cups

Ingredients

600 ml/1 pint natural yogurt

few drops of almond extract

2–3 tsp clear honey, warmed

55 g/2 oz whole blanched almonds

175 g/6 oz no-soak dried apricots

Nutritional Fact

Apricots contain good amounts of fibre and are famed for clearing out the bowel and therefore the body; try to buy the unsulphured variety of these and all dried fruits to avoid stomach upsets.

Serving Analysis

- *Calories*   *88*
- *Protein*   *3.4g*
- *Carbohydrate*   *10.5g*
- *Sugars*   *10g*
- *Fat*   *3.7g*
- *Saturates*   *1g*
- *GI*   *Low*

1 Line a 12-cup bun tin with small paper cake cases.

2 Spoon the yogurt into a mixing bowl, add the almond extract and honey and stir well.

3 Using a small, sharp knife, cut the almonds into very thin slivers and stir into the yogurt mixture.

4 Using a pair of kitchen scissors, cut the apricots into small pieces, then stir into the yogurt.

5 Spoon the mixture into the paper cases and freeze for 1 1/2–2 hours, or until just frozen. Serve immediately.

serves 6

Aromatic Pears

Ingredients

2 tbsp clear honey

450 ml/16 fl oz cold water

2 whole star anise

1 cinnamon stick, lightly bruised, plus extra to decorate (optional)

4 whole cloves

10-cm/4-inch strip of thinly pared orange rind

6 semi-ripe pears

300 ml/10 fl oz Greek-style yogurt

1 tbsp orange juice

2 tsp finely grated orange rind

1/2–1 tsp ground cinnamon

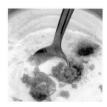

Nutritional Fact
Pears, like apples, contain pectin, a type of fibre that slows down the release of food after meals, removes unwanted toxins and helps lower cholesterol.

Serving Analysis

- Calories   162
- Protein   2.8g
- Carbohydrate   35g
- Sugars   26g
- Fat   2.6g
- Saturates   1.1g
- GI   Low

1 Put the honey, water, spices and thinly pared orange rind into a large saucepan or frying pan over a low heat and heat, stirring, until the honey has dissolved. Bring to the boil and boil gently for 5 minutes, then reduce the heat and simmer while peeling the pears.

2 Thinly peel the pears, keeping the stalks in place, and add to the syrup. Add to the pan, cover and cook over a low heat, turning the fruit occasionally, for 15–20 minutes, or until the pears are tender when gently pierced with a small, sharp knife. Remove from the heat, keep covered with the lid or a large piece of foil and leave until cool – about 1 hour – turning the pears occasionally in the syrup.

3 Meanwhile, blend the yogurt with the orange juice and rind and cinnamon in a serving bowl, cover and chill in the refrigerator until required.

4 Serve the pears, with some of the syrup poured over, with the yogurt. Decorate with cinnamon sticks, if desired.

serves 6–8

Apple & Elderflower Dessert

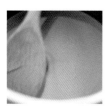

Nutritional Fact

Honey is a sugar essentially made from flowers and has a lower GI value than sugar. Choose one from a single source rather then a blended variety and you will benefit from its healing properties.

Serving Analysis

- *Calories*   74
- *Protein*   1.8g
- *Carbohydrate*   17g
- *Sugars*   14g
- *Fat*   0.01g
- *Saturates*   0.0g
- *GI*   Medium

1 Put the fruit juice into a medium-size saucepan. Stir in the honey, then sprinkle the gelatine over the surface. Place over a low heat and slowly bring to the boil, whisking constantly with a balloon whisk. When the mixture is just boiling, remove from the heat and leave to cool at room temperature for 3–4 hours until it starts to set.

2 Meanwhile, prepare the fruit. If using melons, cut into slices, remove and discard the seeds and skin, then cut the flesh into small pieces. If using grapes, wash and dry thoroughly and remove from the stalks. Cut in half if large. Reserve.

3 Once the jelly is beginning to set, stir the prepared fruit into the jelly and then spoon carefully into either a glass serving bowl or individual glass serving dishes or wine glasses.

4 Leave to set in the refrigerator for about 2 hours, then serve.

Ingredients

450 ml/16 fl oz apple and elderflower fruit juice

1–2 tbsp clear honey

11 g (1/4 oz) sachet gelatine

3 tbsp Cointreau or brandy, or extra fruit juice

450 g/1 lb fruit, such as Galia and Ogen melon and green and red seedless grapes

serves 4

Iced Raspberry Sundae

Ingredients

450 g/1 lb fresh raspberries, plus extra to decorate

450 ml/16 fl oz double cream

55 g/2 oz flaked almonds

225 g/8 oz fresh stoned or canned cherries

15 g/¹/₂ oz plain dark chocolate, coarsely grated

fresh mint sprigs, to garnish

1 Preheat the oven to 200°C/400°F/Gas Mark 6. Reserve 115 g/4 oz of the raspberries and lightly crush the remainder.

2 Whip the cream in a medium-size bowl until soft peaks form. Put 4 tablespoons of the cream into a small bowl, cover and reserve. Stir the crushed raspberries into the remaining cream, spoon into a freezerproof container and freeze for 1 hour, or until partially frozen.

3 Meanwhile, spread the almonds out on a baking sheet and toast in the preheated oven, turning occasionally, for 8–10 minutes, or until golden brown. Remove from the oven and leave to cool.

4 Arrange the reserved raspberries and cherries in the bases of 4 sundae glasses, then sprinkle with a few toasted almonds. Cover with scoops of the frozen raspberry mixture, then either pipe or swirl the reserved cream on top. Sprinkle with the grated chocolate and decorate with extra raspberries and mint sprigs.

Nutritional Fact

Dark chocolate contains plant chemicals called catechins, which are potent antioxidants and therefore protect the body against damage and disease.

Serving Analysis

- *Calories*   597
- *Protein*   7.2g
- *Carbohydrate*   26g
- *Sugars*   18g
- *Fat*   54g
- *Saturates*   29g
- *GI*   Low

makes 9 squares

Fruit & Nut Squares

Nutritional Fact
Oats release their sugars very slowly and have a low GI value; they have an excellent ability to normalize blood sugar and their fat content creates heat in the body.

Serving Analysis
- *Calories*   296
- *Protein*   6.7g
- *Carbohydrate*   22g
- *Sugars*   13.3g
- *Fat*   22g
- *Saturates*   7.6g
- *GI*   Low

1 Preheat the oven to 180°C/350°F/Gas Mark 4. Lightly grease an 18-cm/7-inch shallow, square baking tin with butter. Beat the remaining butter with the honey in a bowl until creamy, then beat in the egg with the almonds.

2 Add the remaining ingredients and mix together. Press into the prepared tin, ensuring that the mixture is firmly packed. Smooth the top.

3 Bake in the preheated oven for 20–25 minutes, or until firm to the touch and golden brown.

4 Remove from the oven and leave for 10 minutes before marking into squares. Leave until cold before removing from the tin. Store in an airtight container.

Ingredients

115 g/4 oz unsalted butter, plus extra for greasing

2 tbsp clear honey

1 egg, beaten

85 g/3 oz ground almonds

115 g/4 oz no-soak dried apricots, finely chopped

55 g/2 oz dried cherries

55 g/2 oz toasted chopped hazelnuts

25 g/1 oz sesame seeds

85 g/3 oz jumbo porridge oats

makes 14–16 bars

Carrot Bars

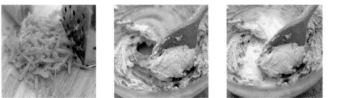

Ingredients

sunflower oil, for oiling

175 g/6 oz unsalted butter

85 g/3 oz light muscovado sugar

2 eggs, beaten

55 g/2 oz self-raising wholemeal flour, sifted

1 tsp baking powder, sifted

1 tsp ground cinnamon, sifted

115 g/4 oz ground almonds

115 g/4 oz carrot, coarsely grated

85 g/3 oz sultanas

85 g/3 oz no-soak dried apricots, finely chopped

55 g/2 oz toasted chopped hazelnuts

1 tbsp flaked almonds

Nutritional Fact
Cinnamon helps the body to use insulin more effectively by helping fat cells recognize and respond to it; cooking does not affect its potency.

Serving Analysis

• *Calories*   *234*
• *Protein*   *4.2g*
• *Carbohydrate*   *19.5g*
• *Sugars*   *13.5g*
• *Fat*   *17g*
• *Saturates*   *6.7g*
• *GI*   *Medium*

1 Preheat the oven to 180°C/350°F/Gas Mark 4. Lightly oil and line a 25- x 20-cm/10- x 8-inch shallow, rectangular baking tin with non-stick baking paper.

2 Cream the butter and sugar together in a bowl until light and fluffy, then gradually beat in the eggs, adding a little flour after each addition.

3 Add all the remaining ingredients, except the flaked almonds. Spoon the mixture into the prepared tin and smooth the top. Sprinkle with the flaked almonds.

4 Bake in the preheated oven for 35–45 minutes, or until the mixture is cooked and a skewer inserted into the centre comes out clean.

5 Remove from the oven and leave to cool in the tin. Remove from the tin, discard the lining paper and cut into bars.

Index